SOUNDS OF LANGUAGE

readers

SOUNDS of a POWWOW

by Bill Martin Jr.
IN COLLABOR-ATION WITH Peggy Brogan

ACKNOWLEDGMENTS

The Author and Holt, Rinehart and Winston, Inc., thank the following authors and publishers, whose help and permissions to reprint materials have made this book possible. All reasonable effort has been made to locate the source of every selection. If any errors in acknowledgments have occurred, they were inadvertent and will be corrected in subsequent editions as they are realized.

Marjorie Barrows, for "Witches' Chant," adapted from "Halloween," by Marjorie Barrows.

Michael Brent Publications, Inc., for "The Marshmallow Bunny," by Ruth Roberts. Copyright © 1965 by Michael Brent Publications.

Leo Feist, Inc., for "K-K-K-Katy," by Geoffrey O'Hara. Copyright 1918, 1945 by Leo Feist, Inc.

Harcourt, Brace and World, Inc., for a selection from *The People, Yes*, by Carl Sandburg. Copyright 1936 by Harcourt, Brace and World, Inc. Copyright © 1964 by Carl Sandburg. Reprinted by permission of the publisher.

Hill and Range Songs, Inc., and Anne-Rachel Music Corp., for "Three Little Fishes," by Saxie Dowell. Copyright 1939 by Anne-Rachel Music Corp.

Holt, Rinehart and Winston, Inc., for *David Was Mad!*, by Bill Martin Jr. Copyright © 1967 by Holt, Rinehart and Winston.

Houghton Mifflin, Inc., for "Grizzly Bear," by Mary Austin, from *The Children Sing in the Far West*, by Mary Austin. Copyright © 1956 by Kenneth M. Chapman and Mary C. Wheelwright.

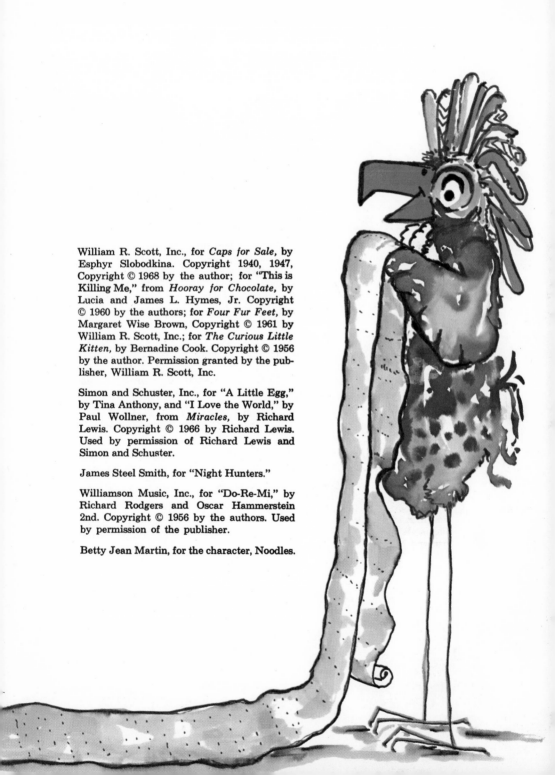

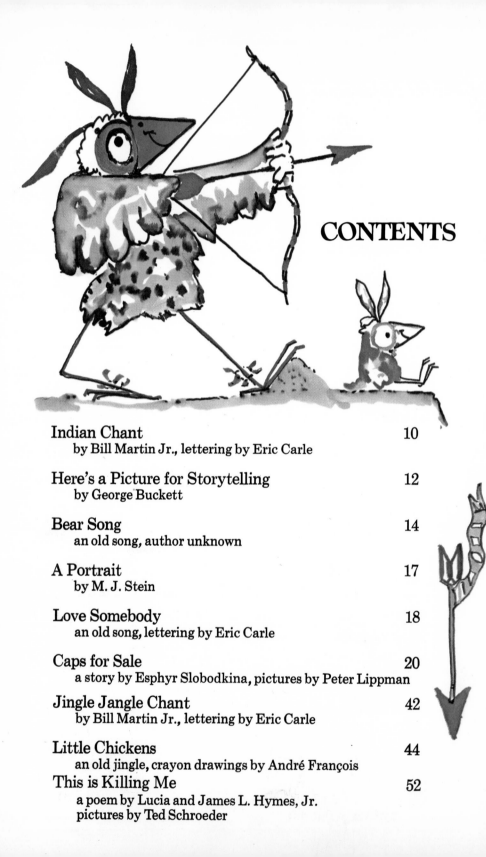

CONTENTS

BEAT BEAT

BEAT BEAT

BEAT BEAT

BEAT BEAT

SHUFFLE to the LEFT

SHUFFLE SHUFFLE   SHUFFLE SHUFFLE

BEAT   BEAT

BEAT   BEAT

INDIAN CHANT

to be read like the beat of a tom-tom

by Bill Martin Jr.   lettering by Eric Carle

BEAT upon the TOM TOM
BEAT upon the DRUM
BEAT upon the TOM TOM
BEAT upon the DRUM

SHUFFLE to the LEFT
SHUFFLE to the LEFT
BEAT upon the TOM TOM
BEAT upon the DRUM

Here's a Picture for Storytelling
by George Buckett

THE BEAR SONG

To be chanted as a two-part choral reading. Sometimes the second group echoes the first group, but at other times both groups read together, as the type indicates.

THE OTHER DAY

the other day

I MET A BEAR

I met a bear

OUT IN THE WOODS

out in the woods

A WAY OUT THERE.

a way out there.

THE OTHER DAY I MET A BEAR OUT IN THE WOODS A WAY OUT THERE

OUT IN THE WOODS.

out in the woods.

A WAY OUT THERE.

a way out there.

HE LOOKED AT ME,
he looked at me,

I LOOKED AT HIM,
I looked at him,

HE SIZED ME UP,
he sized me up,

I SIZED UP HIM,
I sized up him,

HE LOOKED AT HIM, HE SIZED ME UP, I SIZED UP HIM,

HE LOOKED AT ME, I LOOKED AT HIM,
HE SIZED ME UP,
he sized me up,

I SIZED UP HIM,
I sized up him.

an old song, author unknown

NOW THAT YOU HAVE THE PATTERN

for making a two-part choral
reading of this old jingle,
you're on your own for
the last two verses. Good luck!

He said to me, "Why don't you run?
I see you ain't got any gun."
He said to me, "Why don't you run?
I see you ain't got any gun.
I see you ain't got any gun."

I said to him, "That's a good idea,
So come on feet, let's up and fleet."
I said to him, "That's a good idea,
So come on feet, let's up and fleet.
So come on feet, let's up and fleet."

Young Cowboy by M. J. Stein

LOVE SOMEBODY,
LOVE SOMEBODY,
LOVE SOMEBODY,
LOVE SOMEBODY,

AND I HOPE SOMEBODY

YES I DO,
YES I DO,
YES I DO,
YES I DO,

This song can have as many verses as you wish, just by making up new words for YES I DO.

Here are some possibilities:
CAN'T GUESS WHO
LOOKS LIKE YOU
EYES OF BLUE

LOVES ME TOO.

an old song, lettering by Eric Carle

CapsforSale

a STORY
BY ESPHYR
SLOBODKINA

Once there was a peddler
who went out to sell caps.
He carried the caps
on top of his head.

First he put on his own striped cap,
then four yellow caps,
then four blue caps,
then four red caps,
and on the very top four polkadot caps.

Pixs by
Peter Lippman

He walked up and down the streets,
holding himself very straight
so as not to upset his caps.

As he went along he called,
"Caps! Caps for sale! Fifty cents a cap!"

But nobody bought any caps that morning.
Not even a red cap.

In time the peddler began to feel
    very hungry,
but he had no money for lunch.
Not even for a taco.

So he walked and walked
until he came to a great big tree.
"This is a nice place to rest,"
    thought he.

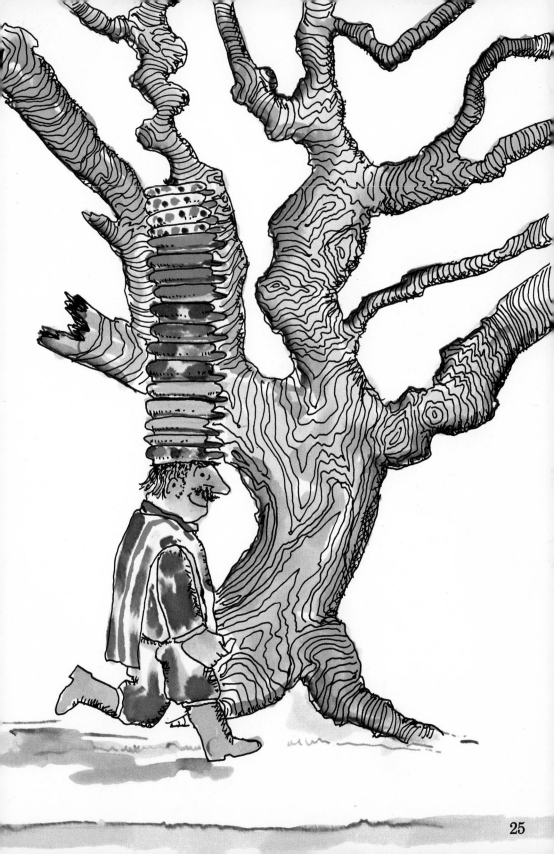

So he sat down, under the tree
and leaned back
little by little
against the tree-trunk
so as not to upset the caps on his head.

Then he reached up
to make sure that they were straight—
first his own striped cap,
then the four yellow caps,
then the four blue caps,
then the four red caps,
then on the very top the four polkadot caps.

Then he went to sleep.

He slept for a long time.

When he woke up,
he reached up to make sure
that his caps were still on his head.

All he felt was his own striped cap!
The other caps were gone.

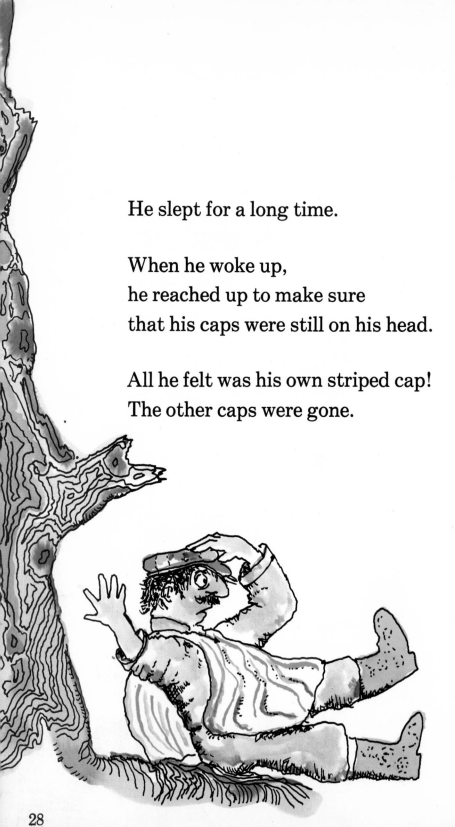

He looked to the right of him.
No caps.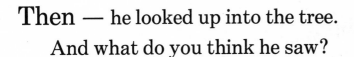

He looked to the left of him.
No caps.

He looked in back of him.
No caps.

He looked behind the tree.
No caps.

Then — he looked up into the tree.
And what do you think he saw?

On every branch there was a monkey.

On every monkey there was a cap—
a yellow cap, or a blue cap, or a red cap,
or a polkadot cap!

The peddler looked at the monkeys.

The monkeys looked at the peddler.

He shook a finger at the monkeys and said,
"You monkeys, you! Give me back my caps!"

The monkeys only shook their fingers back
at him and said, "Tsz, tsz, tsz."

This made the peddler angry,
so he shook his fist at the monkeys and said,
"You monkeys, you!
Give me back my caps."

But the monkeys only shook their fists
back at him and said,
"Tsz, tsz, tsz."

Now the peddler was quite angry.
He stamped his foot, and said,
"You monkeys, you!
Give me back my caps!"

But the monkeys only stamped their feet
back at him and said,
"Tsz, tsz, tsz."

At last the peddler became so angry

that he pulled off his cap

and threw it on the ground.

Then, each monkey pulled off his cap…

and all the yellow caps…

and all the blue caps…

and all the red caps…

and all the polkadot caps…

came flying d o w n o u t of the tree.

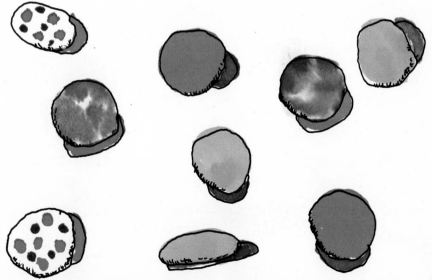

So the peddler picked up his caps
    and put them back on his head—

first his own striped cap,

then the four yellow caps,

then the four blue caps,

then the four red caps,

then the four polkadot caps on the very top.

And slowly, he walked away calling,

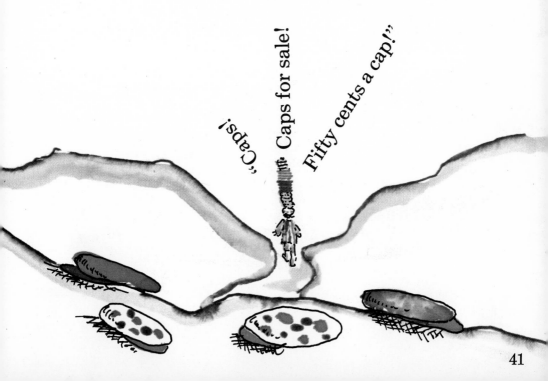

"Caps! Caps for sale! Fifty cents a cap!"

JINGLE JANGLE *JINGLE JANGLE*

JINGLE JANGLE JINGLE JANGLE

JINGLE JANGLE JINGLE JANGLE

JINGLE JANGLE *JINGLE JANGLE*

SHUFFLE to the LEFT

SHUFFLE SHUFFLE   SHUFFLE SHUFFLE

JINGLE JANGLE *JINGLE JANGLE*

JINGLE JANGLE JINGLE JANGLE

JINGLE JANGLE CHANT

to be read like the beat of a tom-tom
by Bill Martin Jr.   lettering by Eric Carle

JINGLE   at the   WRIST BELL

JINGLE   at the   KNEE BELL

JINGLE   at the   WRIST BELL

JINGLE   .at the   KNEE BELL

SHUFFLE   to the   LEFT

SHUFFLE   to the   LEFT

JINGLE   at the   WRIST BELL

JINGLE   at the   KNEE BELL

43

Said the first little chicken
With a queer little squirm,

I wish
I could find
a
fat
little
worm.

an old jingle, adapted

Said the second little chicken
With a queer little shrug,

I wish
I could find
a
fat
little
bug.

with crayon drawings by   André François

Said the third little chicken
With a queer little tug,

I wish
I could find
a
fat
little
slug.

Said the fourth little chicken
With a queer little nod,

I wish
I could find
a
butterbean
pod.

Said the fifth little chicken
With a queer little sigh,

I wish
I could find
a
fat
little
fly.

Said the old mother hen
From the green garden-patch,

If you want
any breakfast,
just come here
and scratch!

I'm too little,
Mother.

I'm too busy,
Mother.

I can't scratch,
Mother.

50

I'm not hungry,
Mother.

Boo hoo!

by Lucia and James L. Hymes, Jr. with pictures by Ted Schroeder

GO SCRUB YOUR FACE AND WASH YOUR HANDS

Mother says
to me.

I scrub my face,
wash my hands,

And come to let her see.

GO SCRUB YOUR FACE AND WASH YOUR HA

She says again
to me.

I scrub my face,
wash my hands,

But this is killing me!

53

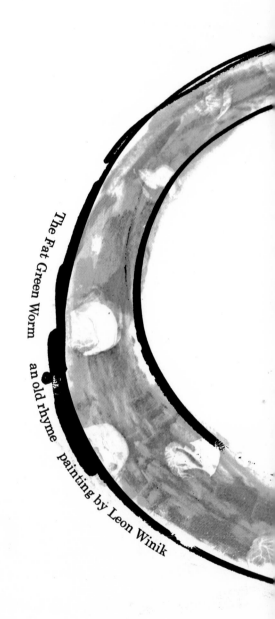

The Fat Green Worm   an old rhyme   painting by Leon Winik

I WON IT,
YOU TWO IT,
I THREE IT,
YOU FOUR IT,
I FIVE IT,
YOU SIX IT,
I SEVEN IT,

YOU EIGHT IT!

Here's a Picture to Dream About by E. Garcia Yata

In the night,
   opossum;
in the night,
the owl;
in the night
the bat—
and coyote
on the prowl.

In the day
   the butterfly;
in the day
the bee;
in the day
the hummingbird—
and a deer
beneath a tree.

a poem by James Steel Smith

a song by Geoffrey O'Hara,   picture by George Buckett

K-K-K-Katy,
beautiful Katy,
you're the only
g-g-g-girl
that I adore.
When the m-moon
shines
over the cow shed,
I'll be waiting at
the kitty-k-kitchen
door.

Once   was   a   peddler

$$\begin{bmatrix} \textbf{One day} \\ \text{Long ago} \end{bmatrix} \text{there} \begin{bmatrix} \text{were} \end{bmatrix} \begin{bmatrix} \text{two} \\ \textbf{many} \end{bmatrix} \begin{bmatrix} \text{dog (s)} \\ \text{monkey (s)} \\ \text{ghost (s)} \\ \text{pieman} \\ \text{piemen} \end{bmatrix}$$

PUZZLE

	went	out	to sell	caps.
	flew	in	to eat	cookies
	jumped	by	to scare	people
who	ran	through	to cook	spinach
	sneaked	about	to make	apples
	crawled		to buy	dirt
				noise
				skeletons

Over in the Meadow

an old rhyme
pictures by Eric Carle

Over in the meadow in the sand in the sun
Lived an old mother turtle and her little turtle one.
"Dig," said the mother.
"I dig," said the one.
So they dug all day in the sand in the sun.

Over in the meadow where the stream runs blue
Lived an old mother fish and her little fishes two.
"Swim," said the mother.
"We swim," said the two.
So they swam all day where the
stream runs blue.

Over in the meadow
in a hole in a tree
Lived an old mother owl
and her little owls three.
"Tu-whoo,"
said the mother.
"We tu-whoo,"
said the three.
So they tu-whoo'd all night
in a hole in a tree.

NOW THAT YOU HAVE READ

the first three verses of this old rhyme,
you can use the clues that follow
to help you figure out
how the rest of the rhyme goes:

1 The first four words of each verse
are exactly the same.

2 The next few words tell where
the creatures live.

 The next few words tell who the mother is and how many babies she has.

 The mother tells the babies to do something and they obey.

 The verse ends by repeating what the babies did and where they were.

NOW, FIGURE OUT THE FOURTH VERSE.

GNAW

Over __ __ __
__ __ old barn door
Lived __ __ __ __
__ __ __ __ __.
     "Gnaw," __ __ __.
     "__ __," __ __ __.
So __ __ __ __
     __ __ __ __ __.

5 Over _ _ _
in a sunny beehive
Lived _ _ _ _
_ _ _ _ _.
        "Buzz," _ _ _.
    "_ _," _ _ _.
So _ _ _ _
    _ _ _ _.

6 _ _ _ _
in a nest made of sticks
Lived _ _ _ _ _
_ _ _ _ _.
"Caw," _ _ _.
"_ _," _ _ _.
So _ _ _ _ _
_ _ _ _ _.

7
_ _ _ _ _
where the grass grows even
Lived _ _ _ _
_ _ _ _ _.
"_," _ _ _.
"_ _," _ _ _.
So _ _ _ _
_ _ _ _.

— — — —
by the old mossy gate
— — — — —
— — — — —.
     "—," — — —.
     "— —," — — —.
So — — — —
     — — — — —.

BASK

9 — — — —
by the old Scotch pine
— — — — —
— — — — —.
     "—," — — —.
     "— —," — — —.
— — — —
     — — — —.

QUACK

72

10

BEAVE

_ _ _ _ _
_ _ cozy wee den
_ _ _ _ _
_ _ _ _ _.
"__," __ __.
"__ __," __ __.
_ _ _ _
_ _ _ _.

THE WORLD on his four fur feet,

his four fur feet,

his four fur feet.

OH, HE WALKED AROUND

And he walked
around the world
on his four fur feet
and never made
a sound—O.

a poem by Margaret Wise Brown
designed by Bill Martin Jr.

OH, he walked along the river
on his four fur feet,
his four fur feet,
his four fur feet.
He walked along the river
on his four fur feet
and heard the boats go toot—O.

THEN he walked by the railroad
on his four fur feet,
his four fur feet,
his four fur feet.
He walked by the railroad
on his four fur feet
and heard the trains go whoo—O.

THEN he waded down a stream
on his four fur feet,
his four fur feet,
his four fur feet.
He waded down a stream
on his four fur feet.
and the water was all wet—O.

THEN he walked into the country
on his four fur feet,
his four fur feet,
his four fur feet.
He walked into the country
on his four fur feet
and heard the cows go moo—O.

SO he folded up
his four fur feet,
his four fur feet,
his four fur feet.
So he folded up
his four fur feet
and lay down in
the grass—O.
And the sun
shone down
on his four fur feet,
his four fur feet,
his four fur feet.
And the sun shone down
on his four fur feet
and made them feel all warm—O.

and never made a sound — O.
on his four fur feet
   And he walked around the world
      his four fur feet.
         his four fur feet,
            on his four fur feet,
            around the world
            walked
            he
            And
            was round — O.
            that all the world
            he dreamed a dream
      And as he slept
      dreamed a dream.
   dreamed a dream,
he dreamed a dream,
   AND as he slept

A Farmyard Song

by Maria Hastings,
pictures by
Sal Murdocca

I had a cat and the cat pleased me,
I fed my cat by yonder tree;
Cat goes fiddle-i-fee.

I had a hen and the hen pleased me,
I fed my hen by yonder tree;
   Hen goes chimmy-chuck, chimmy-chuck,
   Cat goes fiddle-i-fee.

I had a duck and the duck pleased me,
I fed my duck by yonder tree;
　Duck goes quack, quack,
　Hen goes chimmy-chuck, chimmy-chuck,
　Cat goes fiddle-i-fee.

I had a sheep and the sheep pleased me,
I fed my sheep by yonder tree,
   Sheep goes baa, baa,
   Duck goes quack, quack,
   Hen goes chimmy-chuck, chimmy-chuck,
   Cat goes fiddle-i-fee.

I had a pig and the pig pleased me,
I fed my pig by yonder tree;
   Pig goes griffy, gruffy,
   Sheep goes baa, baa,
   Duck goes quack, quack,
   Hen goes chimmy-chuck, chimmy-chuck,
   Cat goes fiddle-i-fee.

I had a cow and the cow pleased me,
I fed my cow by yonder tree;
Cow goes moo, moo,
Pig goes griffy, gruffy,
Sheep goes baa, baa,
Duck goes quack, quack,
Hen goes chimmy-chuck, chimmy-chuck,
Cat goes fiddle-i-fee.

85

I had a dog and the dog pleased me,
I fed my dog by yonder tree;
  Dog goes bow-wow,
  Cow goes moo, moo,
  Pig goes griffy, gruffy,
  Sheep goes baa, baa,
  Duck goes quack, quack,
  Hen goes chimmy-chuck, chimmy-chuck,
  Cat goes fiddle-i-fee.

89

F L

by Jay ELls

The little spaceman came
down &
landed in her backyard.

She took him by the ear &
threw him in
a pit

and grew him like a vegetable.

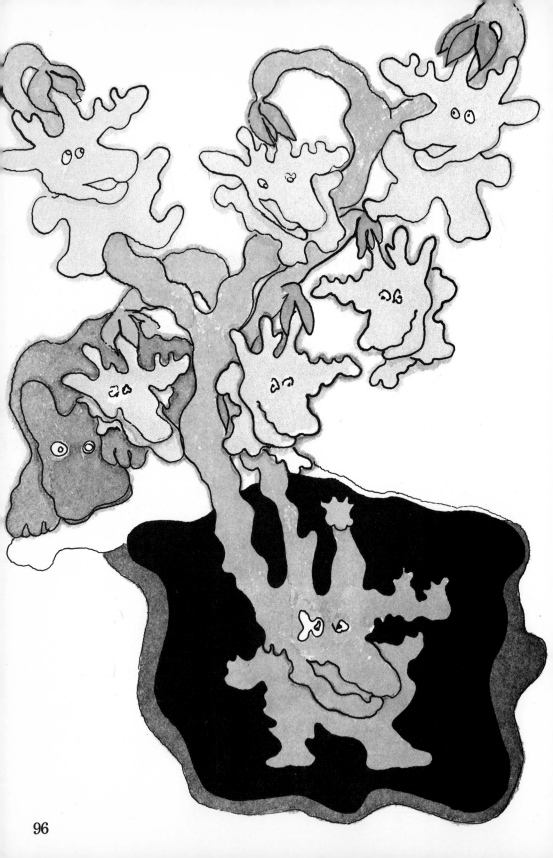

Up he came

by the hundreds.

At her he sprang

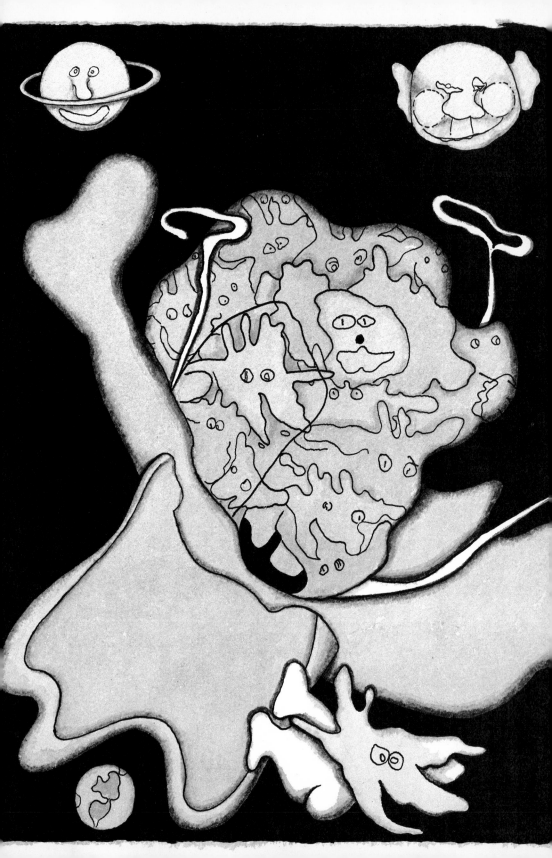

and
took her away in his spaceship

and stuck her in the ground
on his own planet.

She didn't know
what to do;
so she grew;

and when
there was enough of her,

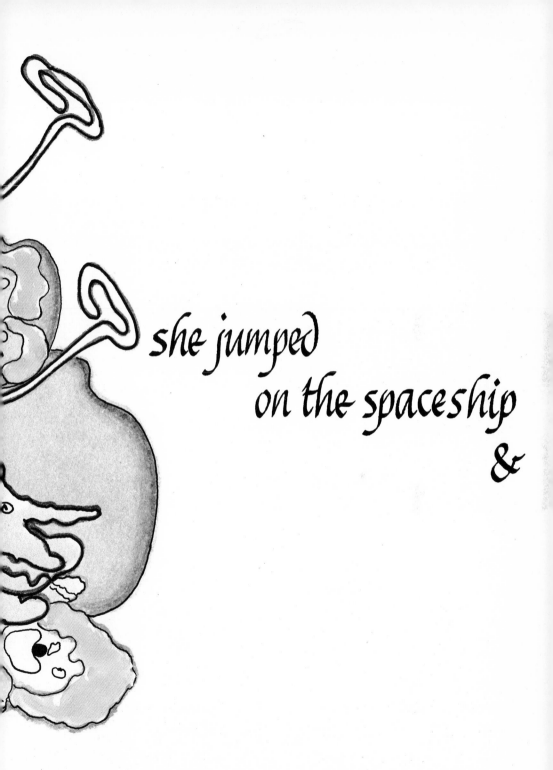

she jumped
on the spaceship
&

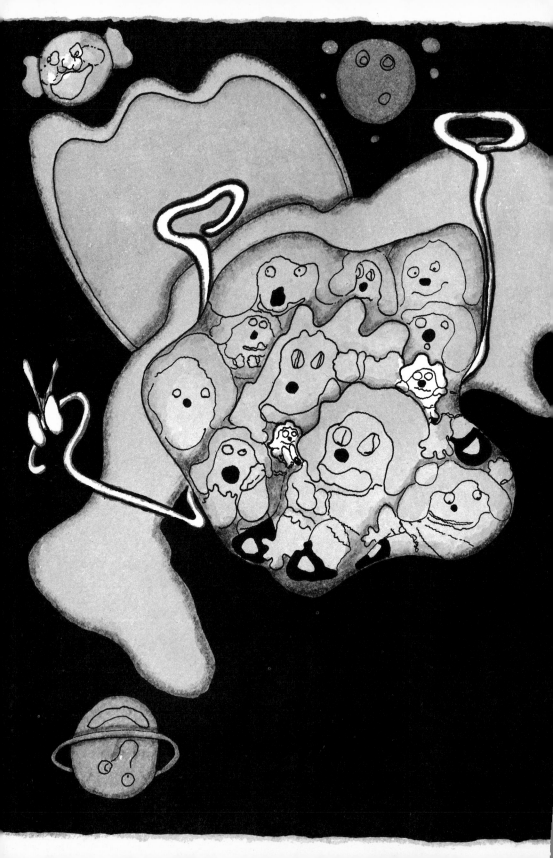

sailed home

and put herself
back together

again.

Spring

Summer

The Four Seasons by Chen Chi

Autumn

Winter

The little girl saw her first troop parade and asked,
     "What are those?"
"Soldiers."
"What are soldiers?"
"They are for war. They fight and each tries to kill
     as many of the other side as he can."
The girl held still and studied.
"Do you know...I know something?"
"Yes, what is it you know?"
"Sometime they'll give a war
     and nobody will come."

From: *The People, Yes* by Carl Sandburg, picture by Henry Markowitz

ONE LITTLE, TWO LITTLE,

FLYING OVER HAYSTACKS,

SLIDING DOWN MOONBEAMS,

HI HO

SHUFFLE to the LEFT,

SHUFFLE SHUFFLE   SHUFFLE SHUFFLE

ONE LITTLE, TWO LITTLE,

HI HO

WITCHES' CHANT

to be read like the beat of a tom-tom
an adaptation from "Three Little Witches" by Marjorie Barrows
lettering by Eric Carle

THREE LITTLE WITCHES,
FLYING OVER DITCHES
WEARING OUT THEIR BRITCHES.
HALLOWEEN'S HERE!

SHUFFLE to the LEFT,
SHUFFLE to the LEFT,
THREE LITTLE WITCHES,
HALLOWEEN'S HERE!

Here's a Picture to Talk About

painting by Ronald Thomason

Ronald

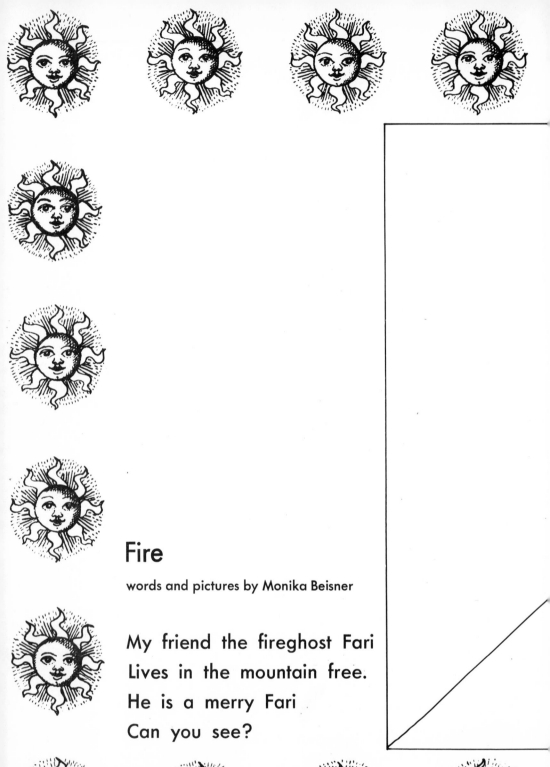

Fire

words and pictures by Monika Beisner

My friend the fireghost Fari
Lives in the mountain free.
He is a merry Fari
Can you see?

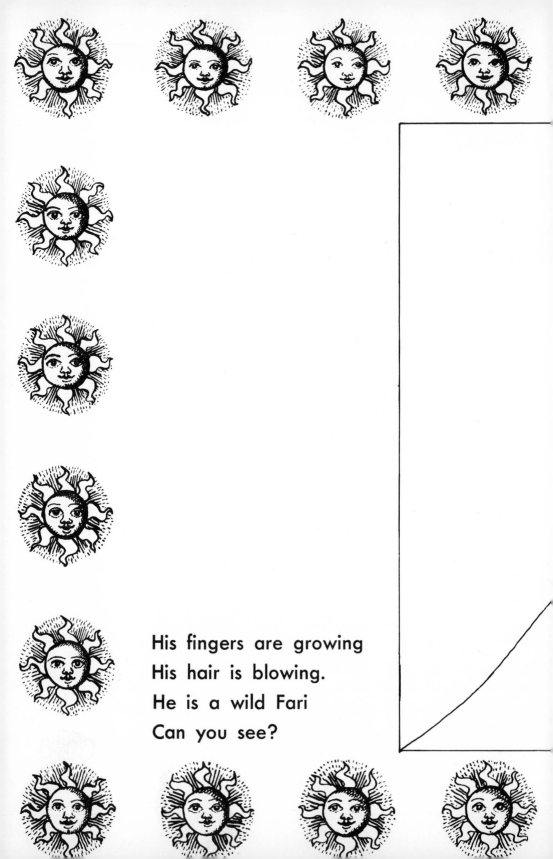

His fingers are growing
His hair is blowing.
He is a wild Fari
Can you see?

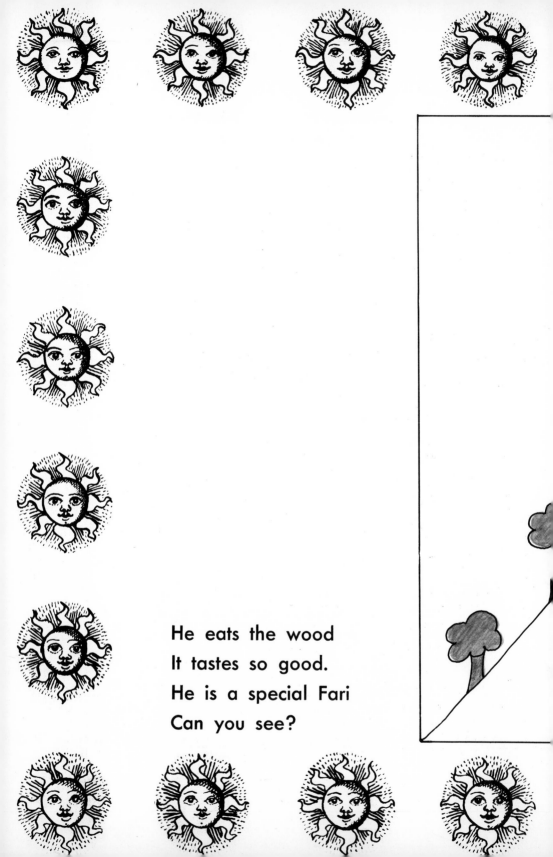

He eats the wood
It tastes so good.
He is a special Fari
Can you see?

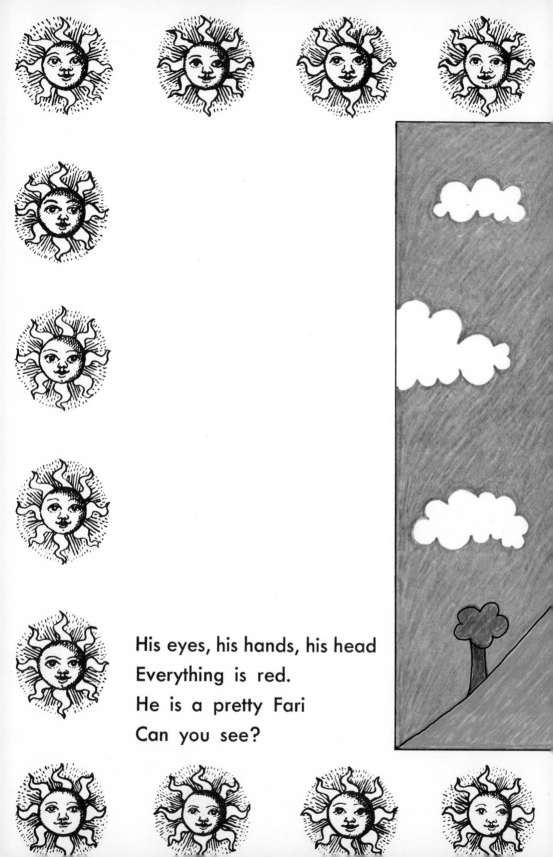

His eyes, his hands, his head
Everything is red.
He is a pretty Fari
Can you see?

Tina Anthony
AGE 7
ENGLAND

Two poems from *Miracles* by Richard Lewis

A little egg
in a nest of hay.
cheep-cheep.
crack-crack.
a little chick
pecked his shell away
cheep-cheep.
crack-crack.

I LOVE YOU, BIG WORLD. I wish I could call you And tell you a secret: That I love you, World... I love you, World...

by *Paul Wollner*

AGE 7

UNITED STATES

A Picture for Storytelling by George Buckett

Once upon a time

there was a turtle.
He wasn't a big turtle,
nor a middle-sized turtle,
but just a little turtle.
And he lived in a small garden
that had a little pool in it.

story *The Curious Little Kitten* by Bernadine Cook, pictures by Remy Charlip

In the house next door
there was a kitten.
Not a big kitten,
nor a middle-sized kitten,
but just a little kitten.
And he was a very curious little kitten
at that.

Every day the little turtle
would walk around in the garden.
Now, turtles cannot go very fast
because their legs are so short.
So they go slowly.
So, the little turtle walked around the garden
slowly, very slowly.
He would stop,
lift up his head,
and then he would go again.

One day

he was walking around like this,

when the curious little kitten
ventured into the garden.

Now, the little kitten
had never seen a turtle before,
because he was just a little kitten
and he hadn't been around very much.
He was surprised.
He stopped and looked at the turtle.

The little turtle stopped.
And the little kitten stopped.

The little turtle looked at the kitten.
And the little kitten looked at the turtle.

Then...

the little kitten slapped at the turtle
with one little paw.
The little kitten's eyes nearly popped right out!
Because—do you know what happened?

The little turtle's head disappeared!
Just like that!
He pulled it right inside
his little turtle shell!

Well!

The little kitten took a step backwards.
And then he sat down.

Pretty soon the little kitten got up,
and walked around the little turtle,
very slowly and very carefully.
He looked at this funny creature
that could make his head disappear.
Maybe, he thought,
if I slap at him again,
his head will come out.

So he slapped him again.
The little kitten's eyes
nearly popped out a second time!
Because—do you know what happened?

The little turtle's legs disappeared!
He pulled them right inside
his little turtle shell.
Well!

The little kitten
didn't know quite what to think.
So he just stood right there,
looking at the little turtle.

And the little turtle sat right there
inside his little turtle shell.

The little kitten
took a step backwards.

And the little kitten
took another step
backwards.

Pretty soon the little turtle
began to let his legs down out of his shell again,
very slowly.

Then the little turtle poked his little nose
out of his little turtle shell.

Then the little turtle poked his whole head
out of his little turtle shell.

And the little kitten took another step backwards.

The little kitten took another step backwards
…and another.

The little turtle took a step toward the kitten.

The little turtle took another step toward the kitten
...and another.

The little turtle took one more step.
And, oh, my!

The little kitten fell

Splash!

backwards
right into the pool of water.

But the little turtle kept right on going,
and slid down into the water,
because turtles just love water.

Now, kittens don't like water
except to drink.
So the little kitten jumped out of the water
and ran past the turtle
as fast as he could run…

…right back home
where he belonged.

But the next morning...

what do you think happened?

GO GO GO TEAM

GO TEAM GETTUM TEAM

GO GO GO TEAM

GO TEAM GETTUM TEAM

SHUFFLE to the LEFT

SHUFFLE SHUFFLE SHUFFLE SHUFFLE

GO GO GO TEAM

GO TEAM GETTUM TEAM

CHEERLEADERS' CHANT

to be read like the beat of a tom-tom
by Bill Martin Jr.   lettering by Eric Carle

gettum gettum gettum TEAM

GO GETTUM *TEAM*

gettum gettum gettum TEAM

GO GETTUM *TEAM*

SHUFFLE to the LEFT

SHUFFLE to the *Left*

gettum gettum gettum TEAM

GO GETTUM *TEAM*

THE TREES ARE BARE, their leaves are off, I hope they're spared the whooping cough.

a verse   by Philip Keils

If you ever, ever, ever meet

a

Grizzly

Bear

You must never, never, never ask him where

He is going,

Or what he is doing;

For if you ever, ever dare

To stop a grizzly bear

You will never meet another grizzly bear.

by Mary Austin

MY FATHER'S FAVORITE BREAKFAST IS HAM AND EGGS.

Author unknown; pictures by Jim and Greg Hildebrandt; lettering by Roy Barber

1

172

ONE MORNING
THERE WERE NO **EGGS**
FOR BREAKFAST
AND THERE WAS NO **HAM**
AND NO BREAD
FOR **TOAST**
AND NO **JAM**
AND NO
CEREAL FLAKES
AND NO
BROWN SUGAR

SO...

MY MOTHER GOT OUT SOME **OATMEAL** AND MADE SOME **PORRIDGE** AND WE ALL ATE **PORRIDGE** FOR **BREAKFAST** JUST LIKE MY DOG'S PORRIDGE AND MY DOG ATE THE **MOST.**

AND WE ALL LAUGHED! AND MY DOG JUMPED UP AND DOWN AND I THINK HE WAS LAUGHING TOO.

Do - re - mi - fa - so - la - ti - do . . .

DOE a deer, a female deer,

RAY a drop of golden sun,

ME a name I call myself,

FAR a long long way to run,

SEW a needle pulling thread,

LA a note to follow sew,

TEA a drink with jam and bread,

that will bring us back to ...

DO ... TI LA SO FA MI RE DO

a song from *The Sound of Music* by Richard Rogers and Oscar Hammerstein 2nd

Do - oh - oh - oh!

Here's a Picture for Storytelling by E. W. Deming

Three
Little
Fishes

a song by Saxie Dowell, with pictures by Sal Murdocca

Down in de meddy in a itty bitty poo,
Fam fee itty fitty and a mama fitty, foo.

"Fim" fed de mama fitty,
"Fim if oo tan."
And dey fam and dey fam all over de dam.

"Top!" ted de mama fitty,

"Or oo ill det ost."

De fee itty fitty dinna anna be bossed.

De fee itty fitty ent off on a spwee,

And dey fam and dey fam ight out to de fee.

"Whee!" 'elled de itty fitties,
        "Ears a wot of fun,
Ee'll fim in de fee ill de day is un."
Dey fam and dey fam and it was a wark,
Till aw of a tudden dey taw a TARK!

187

"He'p!" tied de itty fitties,
        "Dee! ook at all de fales!"
And twit as dey tood dey turned on deir tails!
And bat to de poo in de meddy dey fam,
And dey fam and dey fam bat over de dam.

Boop boop dit-tem dot-tem what-tem Chu!
Boop boop dit-tem dot-tem what-tem Chu!
Boop boop dit-tem dot-tem what-tem Chu!
And dey fam and dey fam bat over de dam.

PUZZLE

Said	first	little	chicken
Cried	second	big	monkey
Roared	last	yellow	mother
Whispered	littlest	sassy	taxi-driver
Shouted	happiest	ugly	pumpkin
Wailed	meanest	spooky	ghost

the

queer

with	a	funny
		long
		scary
		silly

How many different sentences can you make using this sentence for a pattern?

190

squirm,

$$
\begin{bmatrix}
\text{shrug} \\
\text{hop} \\
\text{smile} \\
\text{grunt} \\
\text{groan}
\end{bmatrix}
$$

little

"I wish I could find a fat little worm."

$$
\begin{bmatrix}
\text{I wish I could eat a fat little worm.} \\
\text{I wish I could scare all the children.} \\
\text{I wish I could warm my toes.} \\
\text{I wish I could give you a spanking.} \\
\text{I wish I could put you to bed.}
\end{bmatrix}
$$

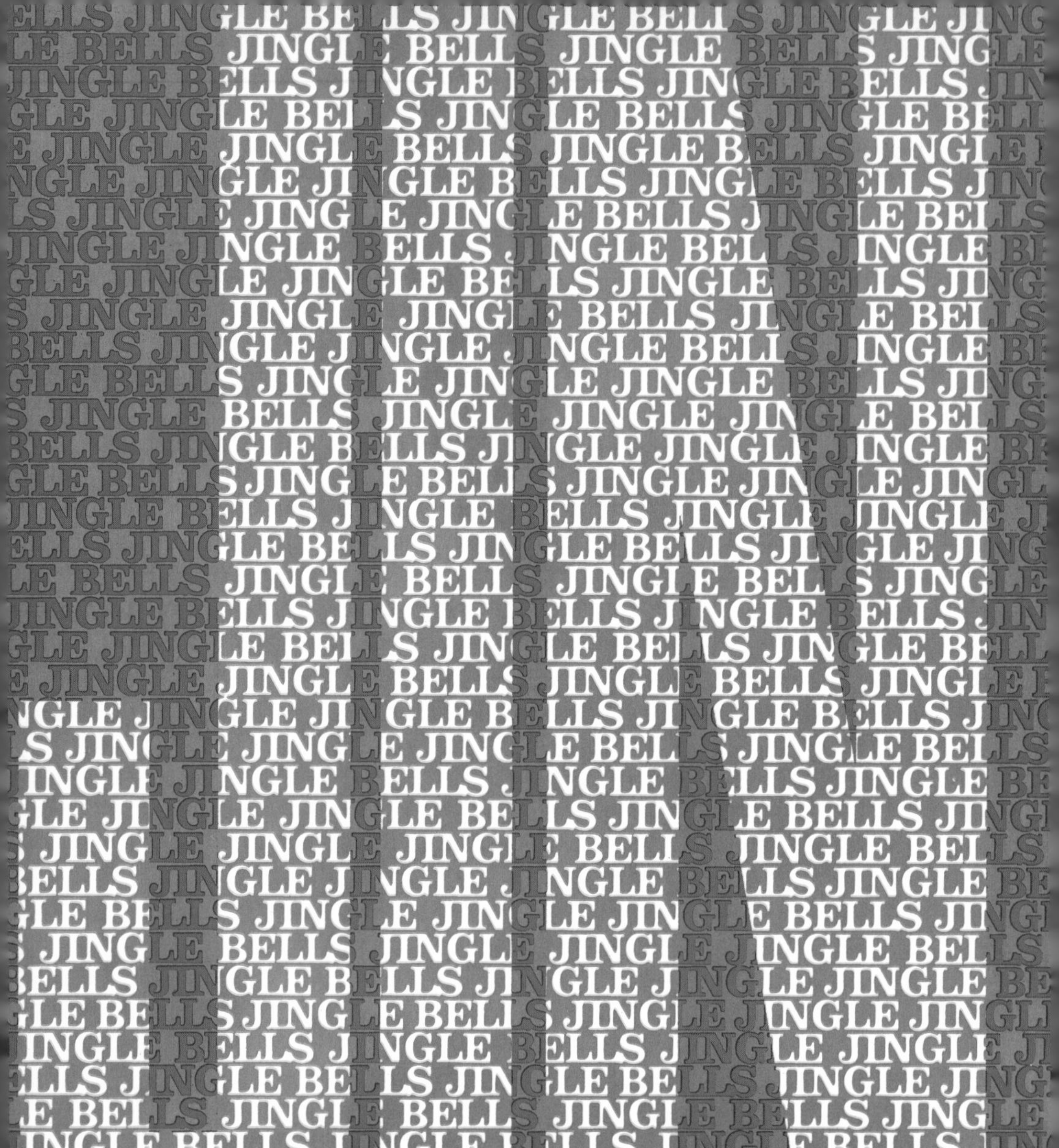
JINGLE BELLS

Jingle Bells

Jingle bells, jingle bells,
Jingle all the way,
Oh what fun it is to ride
In a one-horse open sleigh;
Jingle bells, jingle bells,
Jingle all the way,
Oh what fun it is to ride
In a one-horse open sleigh.

This old man,
He played one,
He played nicknack
on my thumb.
Nicknack paddywack,
Give the dog a bone!
This old man
came rolling home.

an old rhyme, pictures by Cornelio Martinez

This old man,
    He played two,
    He played nicknack
        on my shoe.
    Nicknack paddywhack
    Give the dog a bone!
    This old man
        came rolling home.

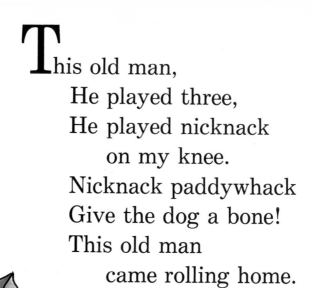

This old man,
He played three,
He played nicknack
on my knee.
Nicknack paddywhack
Give the dog a bone!
This old man
came rolling home.

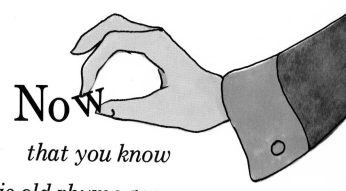

Now,

that you know
how this old rhyme goes
you can say the next seven verses
by knowing the two key words
in each verse:

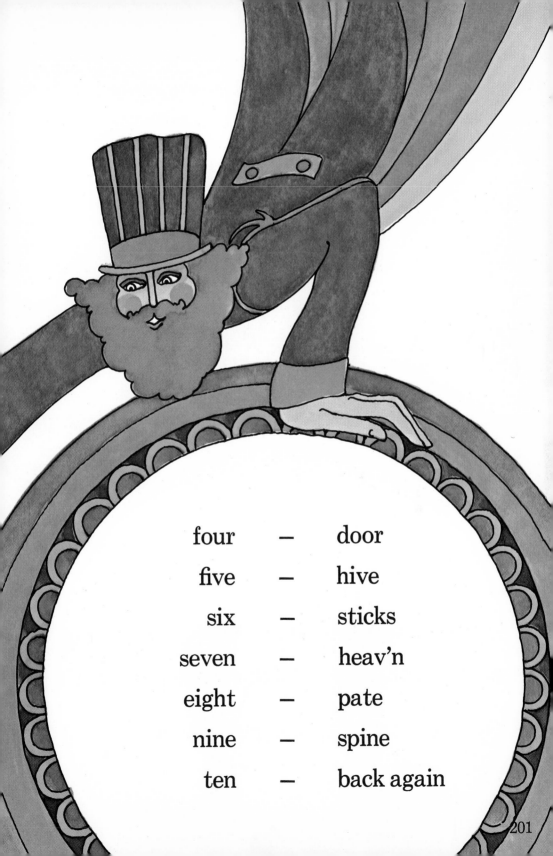

four	–	door
five	–	hive
six	–	sticks
seven	–	heav'n
eight	–	pate
nine	–	spine
ten	–	back again

MISSISSIPPI RIVER MORNING,

MISSISSIPPI RIVER WARNING,

MISSISSIPPI RIVER RAINING,

MISSISSIPPI RIVER WANING,

SHUFFLE to the LEFT

SHUFFLE SHUFFLE   SHUFFLE SHUFFLE

MISSISSIPPI RIVER MORNING,

MISSISSIPPI RIVER WARNING,

MISSISSIPPI RIVER CHANT

to be read like the beat of a tom-tom

by Bill Martin Jr.   lettering by Eric Carle

MISSISSIPPI SUN,
Thunder Wonder DONE,
MISSISSIPPI FLOOD,
OOZY NEWSY MUD,
SHUFFLE to the LEFT
SHUFFLE to the LEFT
MISSISSIPPI SUN,
Thunder Wonder DONE.

The Marshmallow Bunny

by Ruth Roberts
picture by Sal Murdocca

You can take the marshmallows
down from the shelf
And touch them with magic
just known to yourself.
Put them one by one on a barberry twig
with carrots for ears sev'ral inches too big.
Red jelly bean feet and green sugar plum hat.
A marshmallow bunny you can make like that.
With eyes that are raisin, lips that are cherry
and one button tail made of blue huckleberry.

Here's a Picture for Storytelling by Dora Leder

207

Children of the World

English children say *Good morning!*

Mexican children say *Buenos dias!* (Bweh-nohs DEE-ahs)

French children say *Bonjour!* (Bohng-zhoor)

Israeli children say בוקר טוב (BOH-ker tov)

Japanese children say おはよう (O-ha-yo)

Nigerian children say *I putago ula!* (Ee poo-TAH-goo oo-LAH)

German children say *Gutten Morgen!* (Goo-ten-MOR-gen)

Italian children say *Buon giorno!* (Bwohn JOR-no)

Say GOOD MORNING

Puerto Rican children say *Buenos dias!* (Bweh-nohs DEE-ahs)

Chinese children say 早安 (Ts'ow ahn)

Russian children say ДОБРОЕ УТРО! (DOH-broh-yeh OO-troh)

Indian children say नमस्ते (Nah-mahss-TEH)

Norwegian children say *God morgen!* (Goo MOH-rehn)

Portuguese children say *Bom dia!* (Bohng DEE-ah)

Egyptian children say صباح الخير (Sabah el-kh'eir)

a story by Bill Martin Jr., with pictures by Symeon Shimin

DAVID WAS MAD!

He was so angry that he kicked the wall
as hard as he could.
He felt hot—all RED inside.

The cat knew that David was mad.
She knew because David was shouting.

Grandma knew that David was mad.
She knew because David was pouting.

Sister knew that David was mad.
She knew because David hit her.

The teacher knew that David was mad.
She knew because David was scowling.

The children knew
that David was mad.
They knew because
David was arguing.

The children didn't like it,
and they began to argue.
Then they began to feel
all hot and RED inside.

The children got angrier and angrier,
and REDDER and REDDER.

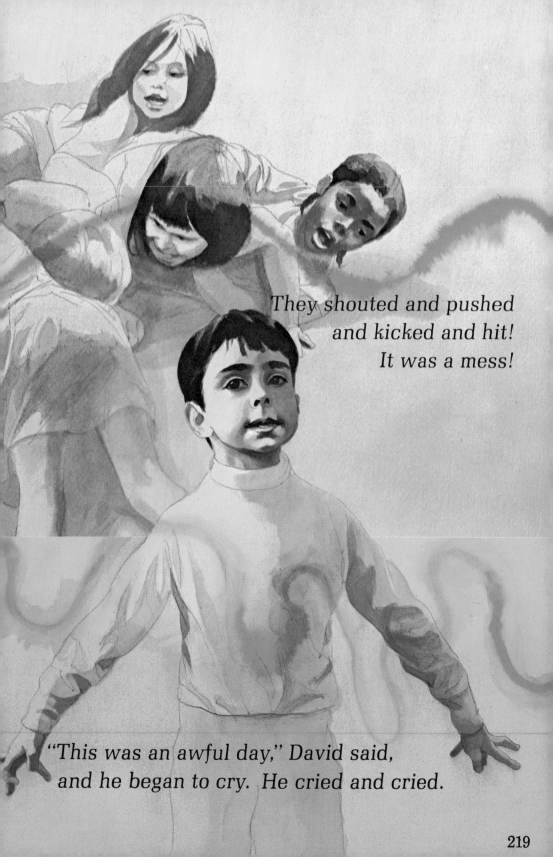

They shouted and pushed
and kicked and hit!
It was a mess!

"This was an awful day," David said,
and he began to cry. He cried and cried.

"I got mad first," David said,
"and then everybody else got mad."
"Yes, that's how it goes," Grandma said.
"Anger is like wet paint.
 It rubs off on everybody who touches it."

Already David was feeling better.
He was beginning to feel all sort of blue
and squishy inside.
His anger had passed.

Here's a Picture for Storytelling

by George Buckett

Navaho Happy Song
painting by Shaner

Hi yo hi yo ip si ni yah,
Hi yo hi yo ip si ni yah,
Hi yo hi yo ip si ni yah,
Hi yo hi yo ip si ni yah,

(Repeat)

Ip si ni *Yah!*

Navaho Indian song